Introduction　　　　　　　　中学校 Version

JN121550

　本書は、長年、中学校で英語授業を行ってきた坂本先生と ALT ミシェルによるティー. ティーチング授業の帯活動をまとめた一冊です。チャンツ、ALT との発音トレーニング. Teacher Talk のリスニング、"友達 Match (Speed Friends)"で文法復習のシンプル英会話、発展的コミュニケーション活動、活発 Negotiation など、付属の QR コードから動画や音声、画像を取得しながら学習できるスタイルです。動画では、ミシェルが Vtuber avatar "Teacher Amy"、坂本先生が"Nami-sensei"となって学習をサポートします。帯活動とは、授業に毎回取り入れる一連の意味を持った活動を指します。帯活動を重ねることで、英語授業にリズムが生まれ、学習者にとって安定した環境と確実な学習の定着を図ることができます。

　また、下のカテゴリー表を用いて、各帯活動が、「読む・聞く・話す［やり取り］・話す［発表］・書く」のどの技能に焦点を当てているか、「知識・技能」「思考・判断・表現」「主体的に学習に取り組む態度」のいずれの力の育成を目指しているかを確認することができ、英語教師にも学習者にも活動の目的が直感でわかるようになっています。4 技能 5 領域＋コミュニケーション力をバランスよく向上するのに役立つ一冊。Now, let's start English class!

youtube.com/c/VirtualEnglish

＜各帯活動が関わる領域と評価の観点＞

	帯活動	4 技能 5 領域					評価の観点		
		読む	聞く	発表	やり取り	書く	知識・技能	思考・判断・表現	主体的に取り組む態度
1	ヒント Quiz	○	○	○	○	○	○	○	○
2	発音 Revolution	○	○				○		○
3	友達 Match (Speed Friends)	○	○	○	○	○	○	○	○
4	探究 Quiz	○	○	(○)	○	○	○	○	○
5	上達 Chants	○	○	(○)			○		○
6	熟練 Sound Connection	○	○	(○)	○		○	○	○
7	納得 Dictation	○	○		(○)	○	○		○
8	伝言 Message	○	○		(○)	○	○		○
9	あいづち Comment Reading	○	○	(○)	○		○	○	○
10	活発 Negotiation	○	○	○		○	○	○	○

ヒント Quiz

Hint Quiz

ここでは、ペアの相手にある「もの・人・動物など」についての説明を英語で行い、クイズをだしていきましょう。

1. ヒント Quiz の答えを考え、短い説明文を３文以上で考える。
2. ペアになってヒントを出し合い、相手の答えを当て合う。

In this activity, students explain an object, person, animal, etc. to their partner in English.

1. Think of an answer and at least 3 sentences to explain it.
2. Make pairs. Listen to your partner's hints & try to guess the answer.

4技能5領域					評価の観点		
読む	聞く	発表	やり取り	書く	知識・技能	思考・判断・表現	主体的に取り組む態度
○	○	○	○	○	○	○	○

< One more try! >

目に見えるもの（pen, apple, dog, restaurant など）から目に見えないもの（dream, AI, job など）まで、幅広くチャレンジしていきましょう。友達どうして発表し合うとより多くのヒントを聞くことになり、次のヒント Quiz づくりを考える「ヒント」がもらえますね。

ヒント Quiz

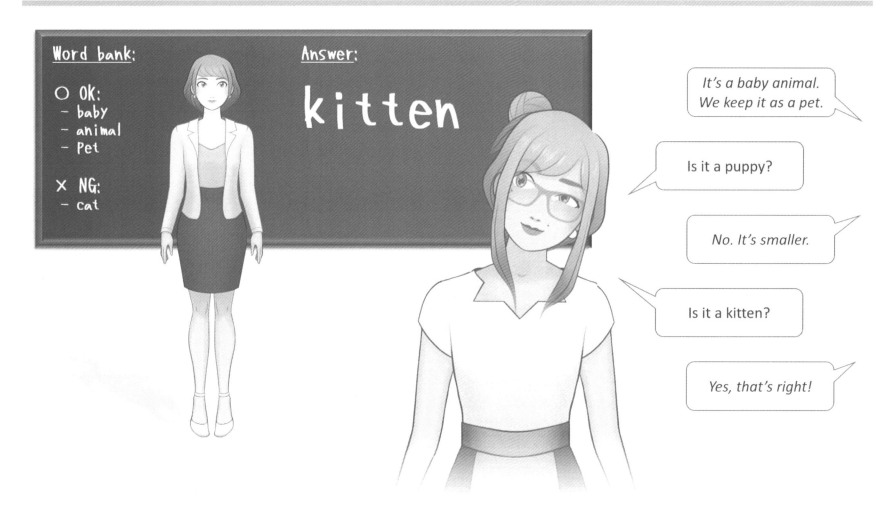

発音 Revolution

Hatsuon Revolution

ここでは、英語の発音を聞き分ける練習をしましょう。

Practice differentiating between similar English sounds.

1. QR コードからアクセスし、音を聞き分ける練習として、その音の違いを意識しながら繰り返す。
2. クイズの音声を聞いて、表の中の聞き取った単語のほうを〇で囲む。
3. 答え合わせをし、結果を表の下段の得点表に書き込む。
4. 音声に基づいたクイズの出題方法をまねしながら、ペアでクイズを出し合う。

1. Access videos by QR code. Listen to the recordings, paying attention to the difference between sounds.
2. Listen to the recorded quiz & circle the words you hear (choose from the table).
3. Check your answers. Calculate your points & write them at the bottom of the table.
4. Try practicing with a partner by imitating the style of the recorded quizzes.

4技能5領域					評価の観点		
読む	聞く	発表	やり取り	書く	知識・技能	思考・判断・表現	主体的に取り組む態度
〇	〇				〇		〇

< One More Try! >

発音の違いに気づいたら、できるだけたくさん自分で発音してみましょう。ペアで出題し合う時は、まず自分の答えを設定し、じゃんけんで出題者と解答者の順番を決めて、互いに出題し合いましょう。口元を隠して発音するのがコツです。

発音 Revolution   ☠ Pi<u>r</u>ate or pi<u>l</u>ot? ✈

Which do you hear, **/r/** or **/l/**?   Circle your answer.

	ROUND 1		2		3		4		5	
Normal (1 点)			r	l	r	l	r	l	r	l
1	right (右)	light (光)	right	light	right	light	right	light	right	light
2	red (赤い)	led (導いた)	red	led	red	led	red	led	red	led
3	wrong (間違った)	long (長い)	wrong	long	wrong	long	wrong	long	wrong	long
4	rice (米)	lice (しらみ)	rice	lice	rice	lice	rice	lice	rice	lice
5	races (競走)	laces (ひも)	races	laces	races	laces	races	laces	races	laces
Challenge (2 点)			r	l	r	l	r	l	r	l
6	pirate (海賊)	pilot (パイロット)	pirate	pilot	pirate	pilot	pirate	pilot	pirate	pilot
7	arrive (着く)	alive (生きている)	arrive	alive	arrive	alive	arrive	alive	arrive	alive
8	brush (筆)	blush (紅潮)	brush	blush	brush	blush	brush	blush	brush	blush
9	fruit (果物)	flute (フルート)	fruit	flute	fruit	flute	fruit	flute	fruit	flute
10	pray (祈る)	play (遊ぶ)	pray	play	pray	play	pray	play	pray	play
		/15 点		/15 点		/15 点		/15 点		/15 点

発音 Revolution ☒ <u>V</u>ote or <u>b</u>oat?

Which do you hear, **/v/** or **/b/**? Circle your answer.

	ROUND 1		2		3		4		5	
Normal (1 点)			v	b	v	b	v	b	v	b
1	vote (投票)	boat (船)	vote	boat	vote	boat	vote	boat	vote	boat
2	vet (獣医師)	bet (賭ける)	vet	bet	vet	bet	vet	bet	vet	bet
3	very (とても)	berry (木の実)	very	berry	very	berry	very	berry	very	berry
4	vow (信約)	bow (お辞儀)	vow	bow	vow	bow	vow	bow	vow	bow
5	vigor (精力、活発)	bigger (〜より大きい)	vigor	bigger	vigor	bigger	vigor	bigger	vigor	bigger
Challenge (2 点)			b	v	b	v	b	v	b	
6	revel (大きいに楽しむ)	rebel (反逆者)	revel	rebel	revel	rebel	revel	rebel	revel	rebel
7	covered (ふたのある)	cupboard (食器棚)	covered	cupboard	covered	cupboard	covered	cupboard	covered	cupboard
8	curve (曲線)	curb (歩道の縁石)	curve	curb	curve	curb	curve	curb	curve	curb
9	dove (ハト)	dub (吹き替え)	dove	dub	dove	dub	dove	dub	dove	dub
10	jive (スイング音楽)	jibe (ジャイブする)	jive	jibe	jive	jibe	jive	jibe	jive	jibe
			/15 点		/15 点		/15 点		/15 点	/15 点

発音 Revolution　　　✝ Fai<u>th</u> or fa<u>ce</u>? ☺

Which do you hear, **/θ/** or **/s/**? (Circle) your answer.

	ROUND 1		**2**		**3**		**4**		**5**	
	Normal (1 点)		θ	s	θ	s	θ	s	θ	s
1	thank (感謝する)	sank (sink の過去形)	thank	sank	thank	sank	thank	sank	thank	sank
2	think (考える)	sink (沈む)	think	sink	think	sink	think	sink	think	sink
3	thin (細い)	sin (罪)	thin	sin	thin	sin	thin	sin	thin	sin
4	thick (厚い)	sick (病気の)	thick	sick	thick	sick	thick	sick	thick	sick
5	theme (テーマ)	seem (〜に見える)	theme	seem	theme	seem	theme	seem	theme	seem
	Challenge (2 点)		θ	s	θ	s	θ	s	θ	s
6	bath (お風呂)	bass (バス［魚］)	bath	bass	bath	bass	bath	bass	bath	bass
7	youth (若さ)	use (使用すること)	youth	use	youth	use	youth	use	youth	use
8	path (道)	pass (パス)	path	pass	path	pass	path	pass	path	pass
9	faith (信念)	face (顔)	faith	face	faith	face	faith	face	faith	face
10	myth (神話)	miss (的を外す)	myth	miss	myth	miss	myth	miss	myth	miss
		/15 点		/15 点		/15 点		/15 点		/15 点	

発音 Revolution　　　　📄 Sheet or seat? ⛏

Which do you hear, **/ʃ/** or **/s/**? (Circle) your answer.

	ROUND 1		2		3		4		5	
Normal (1 点)			ʃ	s	ʃ	s	ʃ	s	ʃ	s
1	sheet (枚)	seat (座席)	sheet	seat	sheet	seat	sheet	seat	sheet	seat
2	she (彼女は	sea (海)	she	sea	she	sea	she	sea	she	sea
3	sheep (羊)	seep (しみ出る)	sheep	seep	sheep	seep	sheep	seep	sheep	seep
4	ship (船)	sip (少しずつ飲む)	ship	sip	ship	sip	ship	sip	ship	sip
5	shin (すね)	sin (罪)	shin	sin	shin	sin	shin	sin	shin	sin
Challenge (2 点)			s		ʃ	s	ʃ	s	ʃ	s
6	mash (すりつぶす)	mass (塊)	mash	mass	mash	mass	mash	mass	mash	mass
7	mesh (網の目)	mess (寄せ集め)	mesh	mess	mesh	mess	mesh	mess	mesh	mess
8	fashion (流行)	fasten (留める)	fashion	fasten	fashion	fasten	fashion	fasten	fashion	fasten
9	fished (釣られた)	fist (拳)	fished	fist	fished	fist	fished	fist	fished	fist
10	crushed (押しつぶされた)	crust (パンの表面)	crushed	crust	crushed	crust	crushed	crust	crushed	crust
		/15 点		/15 点		/15 点		/15 点		/15 点

Which do you hear, **/i:/** or **/i/**? Circle your answer.

	ROUND 1		2		3		4		5	
Normal (1 点)			i:	i	i:	i	i:	i	i:	i
1	green (代の緑)	grin (にこやかな笑顔)	green	grin	green	grin	green	grin	green	grin
2	teen (10 代の)	tin (錫)	teen	tin	teen	tin	teen	tin	teen	tin
3	sheep (ヒツジ)	ship (船)	sheep	ship	sheep	ship	sheep	ship	sheep	ship
4	wheel (車輪)	will (〜するつもりである)	wheel	will	wheel	will	wheel	will	wheel	will
5	seat (座席)	sit (座る)	seat	sit	seat	sit	seat	sit	seat	sit
Challenge (2 点)			i:	i	i:	i	i:	i	i:	i
6	heats (温める)	hits (打つ丘[複])	heats	hits	heats	hits	heats	hits	heats	hits
7	heels (かかと[複])	hills (丘[複])	heels	hills	heels	hills	heels	hills	heels	hills
8	deeper (より深い)	dipper (ひしゃく)	deeper	dipper	deeper	dipper	deeper	dipper	deeper	dipper
9	peeler (皮むき器)	pillar (支柱)	peeler	pillar	peeler	pillar	peeler	pillar	peeler	pillar
10	leaving (leave の現在分詞)	living (live の現在分詞)	leaving	living	leaving	living	leaving	living	leaving	living
			/15 点		/15 点		/15 点		/15 点		/15 点

発音 Revolution
🔪 C<u>u</u>t or c<u>a</u>t? 🐱

Which do you hear, /ʌ/ or /æ/? (Circle) your answer.

	ROUND 1		2 ʌ	æ	3 ʌ	æ	4 ʌ	æ	5 ʌ	æ
Normal (1 点)			ʌ	æ	ʌ	æ	ʌ	æ	ʌ	æ
1	cut (切る)	cat (猫)	cut	cat	cut	cat	cut	cat	cut	cat
2	fun (楽しみ)	fan (ファン)	fun	fan	fun	fan	fun	fan	fun	fan
3	much (たくさん)	match (試合)	much	match	much	match	much	match	much	match
4	bug (虫)	bag (鞄、袋)	bug	bag	bug	bag	bug	bag	bug	bag
5	bun (丸いパン)	ban (禁じる)	bun	ban	bun	ban	bun	ban	bun	ban
Challenge (2 点)			æ	ʌ	æ	ʌ	æ	ʌ	æ	
6	butter (バター)	batter (打者)	butter	batter	butter	batter	butter	batter	butter	batter
7	stunned (あぜんとして)	stand (立つ)	stunned	stand	stunned	stand	stunned	stand	stunned	stand
8	puddle (水たまり)	paddle (櫂)	puddle	paddle	puddle	paddle	puddle	paddle	puddle	paddle
9	begun (begin の過去分詞)	began (begin の過去分詞)	begun	began	begun	began	begun	began	begun	began
10	uncle (叔父)	ankle (足首)	uncle	ankle	uncle	ankle	uncle	ankle	uncle	ankle
		/15 点	/15 点		/15 点		/15 点		/15 点	

発音 Revolution ❄ C**o**ld or c**a**lled? ☎

Which do you hear, **/oʊ/** or **/ɔː/**?   (Circle) your answer.

	ROUND 1		2		3		4		5	
Normal (1 点)			oʊ	ɔː	oʊ	ɔː	oʊ	ɔː	oʊ	ɔː
1	row (列)	raw (生)	row	raw	row	raw	row	raw	row	raw
2	loan (借金)	lawn (芝生)	loan	lawn	loan	lawn	loan	lawn	loan	lawn
3	mole (ほくろ)	mall (モール)	mole	mall	mole	mall	mole	mall	mole	mall
4	goat (ヤギ)	got (get の過去形)	goat	got	goat	got	goat	got	goat	got
5	choke (詰まらせる)	chalk (チョーク)	choke	chalk	choke	chalk	choke	chalk	choke	chalk
Challenge (2 点)			oʊ	ɔː	oʊ	ɔː	oʊ	ɔː	oʊ	ɔː
6	cold (冷たい)	called (call の過去形)	cold	called	cold	called	cold	called	cold	called
7	toast (トースト)	tossed (toss の過去形)	toast	tossed	toast	tossed	toast	tossed	toast	tossed
8	close (閉める)	claws (鉤爪[複])	close	claws	close	claws	close	claws	close	claws
9	bowl (ボウル、椀)	ball (ボール)	bowl	ball	bowl	ball	bowl	ball	bowl	ball
10	rowboat (漕ぎ舟)	robot (ロボット)	rowboat	robot	rowboat	robot	rowboat	robot	rowboat	robot
		/15 点		/15 点		/15 点		/15 点		/15 点	

友達 Match　　　　　　　　　　　　　(Speed Friends)

ここでは、できるだけたくさんの人と会話をして、一番共通点の多い人を探しましょう。

1. 今日の英文1文を声に出して読み、内容を確認する。
2. 「Me」の欄に自分の答えを書き込む。
3. 先生の合図で、一人目の人とペアを組み、じゃんけんをする。勝った人が聞き、負けた人が応える。
4. 聞き手は自分の応えも相手に伝えて、自分の答えと同じだったら○、違っていたらXを表に書き込む。
5. 先生の合図があったら、「Thank you!」と今のペアの相手に伝えて、次のペアへ移る。
6. 5人の相手と会話をしたら、一番○の多かった人について、表の下段に英語で紹介する。

Speak to as many people as possible, searching for people you have the most in common with.

1. Read today's sentence out loud, checking the contents.
2. Write your own answers under "Me."
3. At the teacher's signal, find a partner & play rock, paper, scissors. The winner asks, the loser answers.
4. Both partners should share their answers. If your answer is the same, mark it with a "○". If different, an "X".
5. At the teacher's signal, tell your partner "Thank you!" and make your next pair.
6. After speaking with 5 people, write about your "Top Match" at the bottom of the table.

4 技能 5 領域					評価の規準		
読む	聞く	発表	やり取り	書く	知識・技能	思考・判断・表現	主体的に取り組む態度
○	○	○	○	○	○	○	○

< One More Try! >

相手の質問に1文だけで答えるだけでなく、2文以上にチャレンジしましょう。質問者は、相手の返事にリアクションをしましょう。

友達 Match　　　　　　　　　　　　　(Speed Friends)

No. 1		me	ex. Aika	1	2	3	4	5
①	Do you play any sports?		yes (tennis)					
②	Are you interested in pop music?		yes (idols)					
③	How many pens do you have in your pencil case?		5					
④	What animal do you like?		tiger					
⑤	Can you play any music instruments?		yes (piano)					
	Top Match	"I found …"	"(S)he _likes_ …"	"Both of us _like_ …"		"Neither of us _likes_…"		

友達 Match   (Speed Friends)

No. 2	me	Ayana	ex.	1	2	3	4	5
① Are you good at calligraphy (shodō)?		yes						
② Do you join club activities every day?		no (once a week)						
③ Can you say "生麦生米生卵" three times fast?		no						
④ Which do you want more, a new phone or a new computer?		computer						
⑤ What are your plans today?		relaxing						
Top Match	"I found …"	"(S)he _likes_ …"	"Both of us _like_ …"	"Neither of us _likes_…"				

友達 Match　　　　　　　　(Speed Friends)

		me	Katsunori	1	2	3	4	5
①	What color do you like the best?		green					
②	What do you want for your birthday this year?		a game					
③	Which do you like better, the amusement park or the aquarium?		aquarium					
④	What were you doing at about 7:00 p.m. yesterday?		watching TV					
⑤	Were you busy yesterday?		no					

Top Match　　　*"I found …"*　　*"(S)he likes …"*　　*"Both of us like …"*　　*"Neither of us likes…"*

友達 Match　　　　　　　　(Speed Friends)

No. 4	me	Kokoro	ex.	1	2	3	4	5
① Are you the tallest in your family?		no (shortest)						
② Is pizza more delicious than okonomiyaki?		yes						
③ Is money as important as friendship?		no						
④ Which do you like better, playing sports or listening to music?		music						
⑤ Which season do you like the best?		autumn						

Top Match　　　*"I found …"*　　*"(S)he likes …"*　　*"Both of us like …"*　　*"Neither of us likes…"*

No. 5		ex.	1	2	3	4	5
	me	Ryusei					
① **What time did you wake up today?**		*7 a.m.*					
② **Do you often go to the convenience store?**		*y (every day)*					
③ **What was your favorite animation when you were a child?**		*Winnie the Pooh*					
④ **What is your favorite place in your city?**		*the library*					
⑤ **Do you listen to Western music?**		*yes (pop)*					

Top Match   *"I found …"*   *"(S)he likes …"*   *"Both of us like …"*   *"Neither of us likes…"*

友達 Match   (Speed Friends)

No. 6			ex.	1	2	3	4	5
		me	Taiyo					
①	Have you been living in the same city since you were born?		no					
②	Have you read a book written by Genki Kawamura?		no					
③	Have you been to Universal Studios Japan?		yes (3 times)					
④	Have you ever met a celebrity※? ※芸能人		no					
⑤	Have you been to a bookstore in the last two weeks?		no					

Top Match	"I found …" "(S)he _likes_ …" "Both of us _like_ …" "Neither of us _likes_…"

No. 7		me	Takeshi	1	2	3	4	5
①	Are you interested in the topic of AI?		yes					
②	Which do you like more, the Christmas season or the New Year?		New Year					
③	Which is the more delicious Japanese meal, udon or ramen?		ramen					
④	Which is more important to you in choosing a future job, money or dreams?		money					
⑤	What is the most interesting book that you have ever read?		Harry Potter					

Top Match　　　　"I found …"　　"(S)he _likes_ …"　　"Both of us _like_ …"　　"Neither of us _likes_…"

探究 Quiz   Tankyu Quiz

ここでは、ペアの相手に質問をしていき、相手が想定している単語を当てましょう。

1. 「Word Bank」内の単語を使って、個人で「あるもの・人・動物など」についてヒントを作る
2. ペアになってじゃんけんに勝った人からひとつずつ質問して、答えを探る。
3. 負けた人の返事を聞きながら、勝った人は相手が想定している答えをあてる。

徐々に「Word Bank」内の言葉は少なくなっていくので、後半になるにしたがってオリジナルの質問や回答で答えを探求していく。

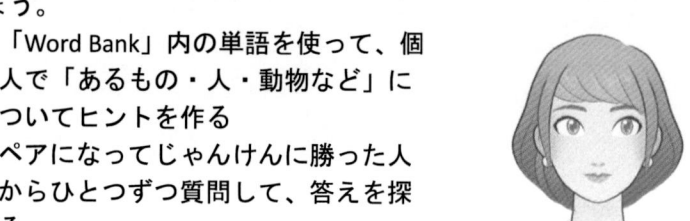

In this activity, ask your partner questions and try to guess the vocabulary word they have chosen.

1. Using the "Word Bank," make your own hints about your chosen topic (thing, person, animal, etc.)
2. Play rock-paper-scissors in pairs. Starting with the winner, ask questions to get hints.
3. While listening to the replies of the other partner, they will try to guess the answer.

As the number of words in "Word Bank" gradually decreases, we will begin to search for answers using original questions and answers.

4 技能 5 領域					評価の観点		
読む	聞く	発表	やり取り	書く	知識・技能	思考・判断・表現	主体的に取り組む態度
○	○	(○)	○	○	○	○	○

< One More Try! >

質問をする際には、Yes/No で答える疑問文から、5W1H(Who/What/When/Where/Why/How)を使って尋ねる疑問文まで幅広く使っていきましょう。

What is this animal?

What continent does it live in? → *It lives in South America.*

What does it look like? → *It has long claws & brown fur.*

What does it like to do? → *It often sleeps in trees.* ※

Choose 2 more animals & use the word bank to write about them!
Your friend will ask you questions & try to guess.

It lives in… North America / South America / Africa / Europe / Asia / Australia and Oceania / Antarctica / Japan / the forest / the mountains / the city

It has… legs / paws / claws / fur / scales / feathers / a tail / wings / fins / spots / stripes

It likes to… play / sleep / eat / hunt / run

It's a(n)… wolf / bear / elephant / camel / snake / owl / leopard / tiger / lion / shark / dolphin / whale / cow / raccoon / fox / koala / turtle

①

②

※ *Answer: It's a sloth!*

探究 Quiz

What is this fish?

What color is it? → *It's orange or white.*
Where can we see it? → *In Japanese gardens.*
Do we eat it? → *No! People enjoy watching this fish.* ※

Choose 2 more fish & use the word bank to write about them!
Your friend will ask you questions & try to guess.

We can see it… at pet stores / at an aquarium / in the sea / in the river / in the lake / in a canal / in rice paddies / at the supermarket / at restaurants
People usually… keep them as pets / keep them in aquariums / enjoy watching them / enjoy feeding them / catch them / eat them
It's a(n)… goldfish / clownfish / shark / betta / angelfish / catfish / guppy / tuna / salmon / bass / eel / Japanese rice fish (medaka)

① ....
....
② ....
....

※ *Answer: It's a carp!*

探究 Quiz

What is this food?

What color is it? → *It's red.*
How does it taste? → *It tastes sweet.*
Where can I get it? → *At the grocery store.* ※

Choose 2 foods & use the word bank to write about them!
Your friend will ask you questions & try to guess.

It tastes… sweet / sour / salty / bitter / spicy / savory / delicious / bad
You can get it… at a (Japanese) restaurant / at a (convenience) store / at a bakery
    / at food stalls / in Italy
We eat it… every day / on New Year's Day / at school / for breakfast / as a snack
It's… an apple / a banana / a potato / French fries / rice / miso soup

①

②

※ *Answer: It's an apple!*

上達 Chants

Jotatsu Chants

一定のリズムにフレーズを乗せて発話し、繰り返してフレーズを何度も聞く活動です。イントネーションや強弱に慣れていきましょう。

In this activity, students repeat phrases several times, following a set rhythm. This helps them get used to intonation & word stress.

1. QR コードからアクセスし、音声を聞く。
2. 音声をまねて発話し、リズムとイントネーションをつかむ。
3. 音声と一緒に発話する。（慣れてくると、ペアやグループで担当箇所をもうけて発話したり、一文ずつ順に回したりしてもよい。）

1. Access videos by QR code & listen to the recording.
2. Mimic the recording, enunciating the rhythm & intonation.
3. Speak with the recording. (After becoming used to it, try doing the chant with a pair or group. It can work well to assign parts or alternate word by word.)

4 技能 5 領域					評価の規準		
読む	聞く	発表	やり取り	書く	知識・技能	思考・判断・表現	主体的に取り組む態度
○	○	(○)			○		○

< One More Try! >

リズムよく言えるようになったら、互いに発表したり、そのフレーズを使った会話をしたりしてみましょう。

Which is Longer?

*   *   *   *
Do, do you know? Please, please, tell me please.

 *   *   *   *
Which is longer, the Nile or the Amazon?

* *   *   *
No, no, I don't know. Let's, let's, ask a friend.

 *   *   *   *
Which is longer, the Nile or the Amazon?

  *   *
The Nile is longer than the Amazon.

  *   *
The Nile is longer than the Amazon.

  * *   *   *
The Nile is longer than any other river in the world!

上達 Chants

The Zoo

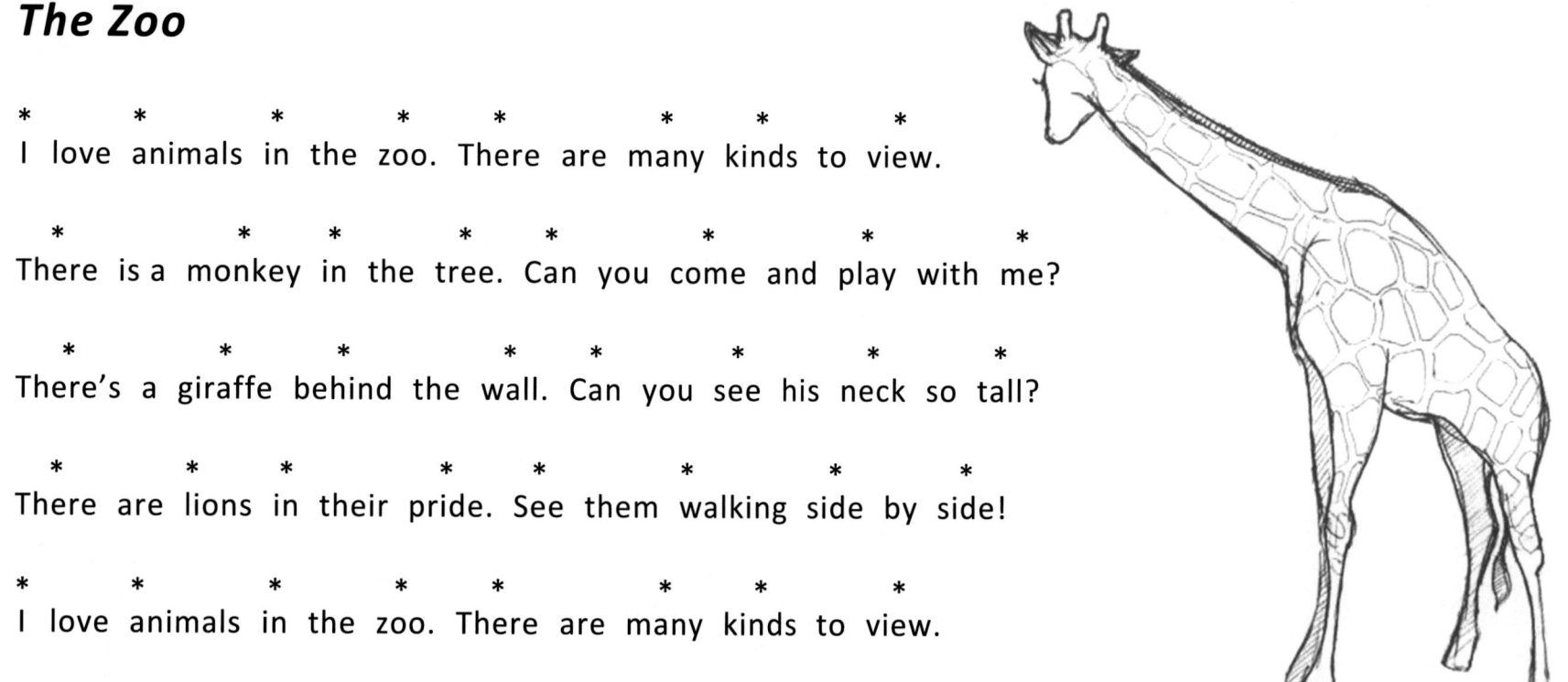

*   *   *   *   *   *   *   *

I love animals in the zoo. There are many kinds to view.

  *   * *   * *   *   *   *

There is a monkey in the tree. Can you come and play with me?

  *   *   *   * *   *   *   *

There's a giraffe behind the wall. Can you see his neck so tall?

*   * *   * *   *   *   *

There are lions in their pride. See them walking side by side!

*   *   *   * *   *   *   *

I love animals in the zoo. There are many kinds to view.

I'm Going to Go to USJ

      *   *   * *   *   *   *
I'm going to go to USJ with my grandmother, mother, and sister.

 *   *   *   *   *   *   *
All of my friends are asking me, "What are you going to do there?"

      *   *   *   *
I'll see an attraction. I'll go on a ride.

          *   *   *   *
    I'll eat all the food I can possibly buy!

 *   *   * *   *   *   *
I'm going to go to USJ with my grandmother, mother, and sister.

上達 Chants

How Long Have You Been in Paris?

A: For more than five years, I've been living in Paris.

B: Oh! What have you done and learned in Paris?

A: I've studied French and painting here.

B: Have you studied them long? For how many years?

A: I've been studying art for at least two or three.

B: And how about French? Since you came to *Paris*?

A: For six and a half. I prepared before then.

B: That's so nice! That's so great! *C'est génial! C'est trop bien!*

上達 Chants

To the Library

```
          *           *           *           *
A:    Excuse  me.  Could  you  help  me  please?

      *           *           *           *
B:    Sure. What  would  you  like  to  know?

              *               *           *     *
A:    Could you  tell  me the  way  to the  library?
          *         *           *         *
      I  don't  remember  where  to  go.

          *           *               *         *
B:    Go  along  the  street  to the  shopping  mall.
              *           *       *       *
      Turn  left  at the  second  traffic  light.
              *           *         *     *
      It's  between  the  park  and  city  hall.
          *       *         *           *
      You  cannot  miss  it  on  the  right.
```

熟練 Sound Connection

Jukuren Sound Connection

ここでは、リンキングを練習し、各文を発端として会話につなげていきましょう。

1. QR コードからアクセスし、音声を聞く。太字のリンキング部分を繰り返し練習する。
2. 自然なイントネーションで発話できているかを確認する。
3. できるだけたくさんの人と会話をする。ペアの相手とじゃんけんをし、勝った人が提示文を使って会話を始める。ペアの間で 2 往復以上の会話ができたら、「Thank you!」と声をかけ、お互いのサイン枠にサインをして別れ、次のペアへ移る。
4. 終了の合図があったら席に着き、サインの数をカウントして記入する。

Here, students will practice linking sounds in a conversation.

1. Access the recordings by QR code. Practice the bold, connected sounds several times.
2. Make sure you speak with natural intonation.
3. Talk to as many people as possible. Make pairs and play rock-paper-scissors. The winner starts. Have a conversation with at least 2 exchanges, then say, "Thank you!" Exchange signatures, then change pairs.
4. When the teacher signals the end of the activity, count the number of signatures you collected.

4技能5領域					評価の観点		
読む	聞く	発表	やり取り	書く	知識・技能	思考・判断・表現	主体的に取り組む態度
○	○	(○)	○		○	○	○

< One More Try! >

英語の音については、いろいろな変化があります。・linking（連結）…単語と単語がつながり、音が連結すること・intrusion（介入）…次の音に介入すること・elision（脱落）…単語の中の発音されるはずの音が発音されないこと・assimilation（同化）…後ろの子音の音とくっついて 1 つの音になったり、子音が変化したりすること・geminates（重複）…音が重複した時に最初の音が軽く発音されること

Connection Type 3: Elision

1) Do you speak to your next-door neighbor? → *nexdoor*	2) What's the most colorful clothing you have? → *moscolorful*	3) Where's the best place to see cherry blossoms in spring? → *besplace*
SIGNATURES:	SIGNATURES:	SIGNATURES:
TOTAL NUMBER:	TOTAL NUMBER:	TOTAL NUMBER:

熟練 Sound Connection

Connection Type 4: Assimilation

1) Won't you tell me what you did yesterday? → *wonʧu / whaʧu*	2) Did you do your homework yesterday? → *didʒu*	3) Would you ever travel to another country? → *wudʒu*
SIGNATURES:	SIGNATURES:	SIGNATURES:
TOTAL NUMBER:	TOTAL NUMBER:	TOTAL NUMBER:

Connection Type 5: Geminates

1) Have you lived here your whole life? → *who**ll**ife*	2) Have you ever had a pet turtle? → *pe**tt**urtle*	3) What's something you like to do? → *what**ss**omething*
SIGNATURES:	SIGNATURES:	SIGNATURES:
TOTAL NUMBER:	TOTAL NUMBER:	TOTAL NUMBER:

納得　Dictation

Nattoku Dictation

ここでは、リスニングを中心に練習しましょう。

1. QR コードからアクセスし、音声ではあるまとまった文章を聞きます。内容を理解しながら英文を聞き、最後の１文を書き取ります。最後の１文は、２度繰り返されます。
2. 全体の音声も２度聞きましょう。
3. 正解は、音声とともに QR コードから確認できます。

Here, let's practice focusing while listening.

1. Access the recording through the QR code. Listen to the English & write the final sentence. The final sentence will be played twice.
2. Listen to the whole recording twice.
3. You can check the answer online.

4技能5領域					評価の観点		
読む	聞く	発表	やり取り	書く	知識・技能	思考・判断・表現	主体的に取り組む態度
○	○		(○)	○	○		○

< One More Try! >

音のつながりに気を付けながら聞き取りましょう。複数回聞いた後、音声に続いて読んでみると音のイントネーションが体得できます。

納得 Dictation

Date:	Date:

Date:	Date:

Date:	Date:

Date:	Date:

納得 Dictation

Scripts

1. 趣味

Nice to meet you. My name is Michelle. My hobby is to play the Japanese drums, taiko. I learned Japanese drums, taiko, in Japan. The sound of taiko is beautiful. I love both listening to and playing taiko. Japanese drums are one of the great cultures in Japan. I played the drums with my team members at concerts in Japan. Do you play any instruments too? Or do you play sports? Do you like to read? ***Now, please let me know about your hobbies.***

2. 日本の建造物

Tokyo Sky Tree is a popular spot for school trip from all over Japan. It attracts many people throughout the four seasons. Every year, about 5,000 schools visit Tokyo Sky tree Town and the Tokyo Sky tree. This beautiful building was opened in Asakusa in 2012. Its height is 634 meters. ***On a sunny day, you can see Mt. Fuji from Tokyo Sky Tree.***

3. 人気のアニメ

Today, I'll tell you about a Japanese manga that is popular all over the world. It is "One Piece". One Piece is a manga that has been in Weekly Shonen Jump since 1997. The main character's name is Luffy. It is a story of a marine adventure, and he and his friends search for the "One Piece." The translated versions have been sold in more than 42 countries. ***Why don't you read it and enjoy the adventure?***

4. 日本の音楽

Have you ever heard of ONE OK ROCK? They are a rock group, and they sing very well. Many of their songs are in English and Japanese. They are one of the popular music groups in Japan. They are famous around the world, too. The father and mother of the main singer were famous singers. Do you like singing? ***Please try to sing their songs in Japanese and English.***

納得 Dictation

5. 行事

On what day of the month is Tanabata? Yes, Tanabata is on the seventh of July. If the night is clear, you can see the Milky Way in the sky.
It is famous for the star story. Orihime and Hikoboshi can meet only once a year. Every year, on the night of seventh of July, people write their wishes written on tanzaku, and hang them on bamboo leaves. Have you ever tried to write on tanzaku? There are five colors of tanzaku, blue, red, yellow, white, and purple. Blue means wood, red means fire, yellow means earth, white means gold, and purple means water. ***What will you write on your tanzaku next Tanabata?***

6. AI 関係

Let's talk about cars today. Will you drive a car in the future? A car is a very convenient vehicle. Many people have a driver's license. So, what will the car of the future look like? In January 2017, a car company, Toyota, announced an interesting car. It is "a car that can talk to people" using AI. If people and cars can talk, it will help people drive safely. In the future, we may see flying cars, too. ***Where would you like to go with a flying car?***

7. 動物

Which animal do you like the most? According to a 2017 survey, the most popular animal in Japan was the dog. 56.3% of people said they liked dogs. Do you like dogs too? Dogs are also a part of the family in the West. There are many movies and books featuring dogs. The second most popular animal was the cat at 44.0%, followed by penguins, dolphins, and pandas. ***Was your favorite animal in the top five?***

8. 世界文化遺産

The Louvre is one of the largest museums in the world. It is a world heritage site and is located in the heart of Paris, France. It is the most visited museum in the world, with over 8 million visitors every year. About 65 percent of the total number of visitors are foreign tourists. We can see many works of art, including the famous painting, "Mona Lisa." Did you know that there is a Japanese exhibit there? It is the Hyakunin Isshu. ***Why don't you visit and take a look at the many works of art?***

伝言 Message　　　　　　　　　　　　　Dengon Message

Amy 先生のストーリーテリングを聞きながら、内容理解を深めていきましょう。

1. QR コードからアクセスし、 Amy 先生のストーリーテリングを聞く。
2. １度目は、何も書かずに流して概要を掴む。
3. ２度目は、ワークブックの英文内の（　　　）にあてはまる語を書き取る。
4. ３度目は、（　　　）内の語を確認しながら、再度聞く。

Listen to Amy's storytelling, focusing on understanding the contents.

1. Access the video recordings through the QR code.
2. 1st Listen: Listen without writing anything to get the overall meaning.
3. 2nd Listen: Write your answers in the blanks in the workbook.
4. 3rd Listen: Check your answers.

4技能5領域					評価の観点		
読む	聞く	発表	やり取り	書く	知識・技能	思考・判断・表現	主体的に取り組む態度
○	○		(○)	○	○		○

< One More Try! >

（　　　）内の語句を確認し、内容が把握できたら、シャドーイングにチャレンジしてみましょう。英語らしい音のつながりやイントネーションを身に付けることができます。

Summer Vacation

This summer vacation, I [(1)] Hokkaido and Tohoku. One of

the places I went to was Akita City. I went there [(2)] some

friends and [(3)] the Kanto Festival. Since childhood, the

performers in the Kanto Festival learn [(4)] balance lantern

poles on their hands, hips, shoulders, and head. [(5)], the

bamboo poles are [(6)] tall, but [(7)] little they

are made taller and taller. It can be dangerous, [(8)] the pole

starts falling or a lantern catches fire, the performers know exactly

[(9)]. They quickly pick up the pole [(10)]

balancing it again. I was so impressed, and had a lot of fun!

伝言 Message

Cat Cafés

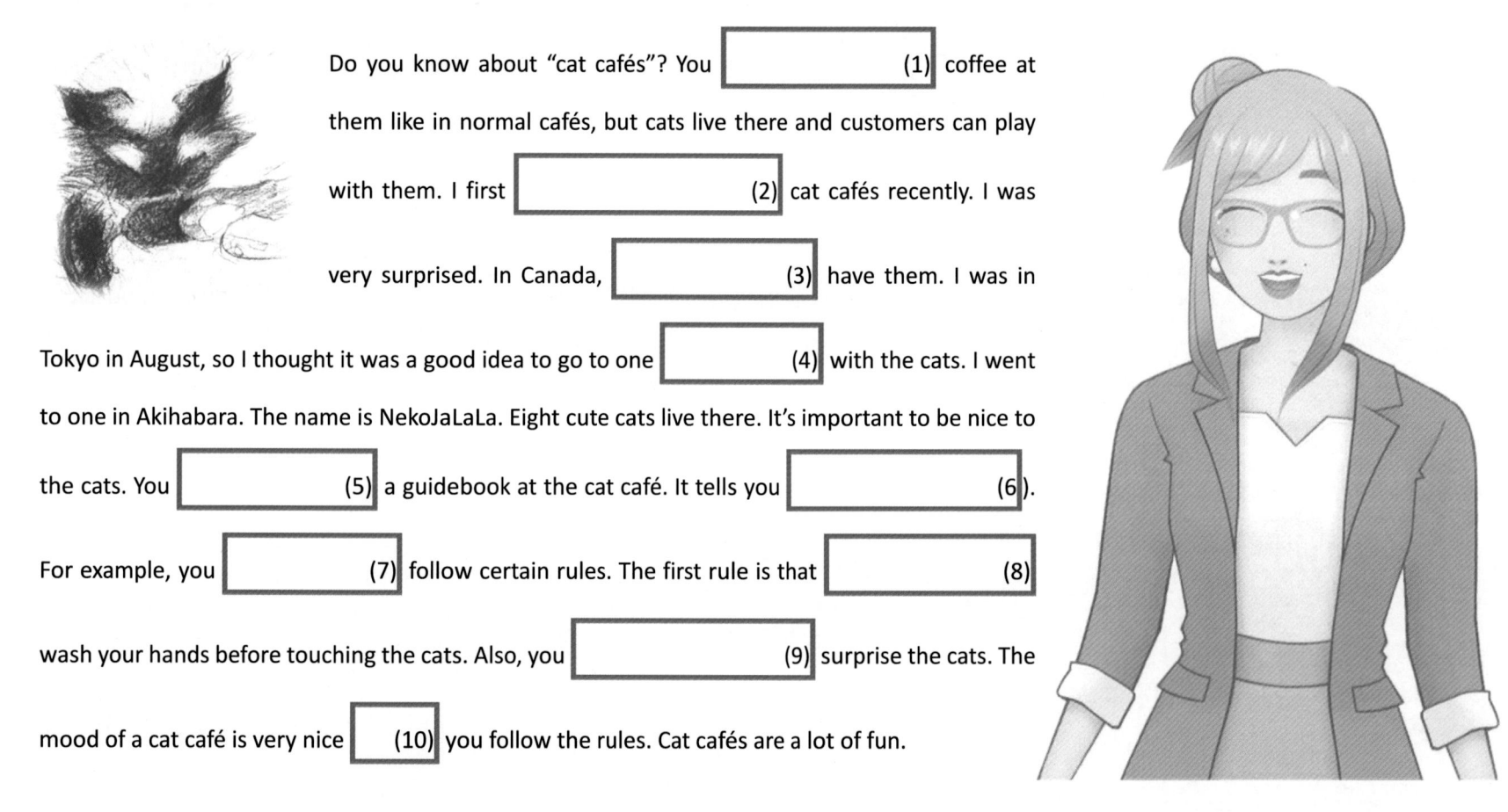

Do you know about "cat cafés"? You _____ (1) coffee at them like in normal cafés, but cats live there and customers can play with them. I first _____ (2) cat cafés recently. I was very surprised. In Canada, _____ (3) have them. I was in Tokyo in August, so I thought it was a good idea to go to one _____ (4) with the cats. I went to one in Akihabara. The name is NekoJaLaLa. Eight cute cats live there. It's important to be nice to the cats. You _____ (5) a guidebook at the cat café. It tells you _____ (6). For example, you _____ (7) follow certain rules. The first rule is that _____ (8) wash your hands before touching the cats. Also, you _____ (9) surprise the cats. The mood of a cat café is very nice _____ (10) you follow the rules. Cat cafés are a lot of fun.

伝言 Message

Scripts

1. Summer Vacation

This summer vacation, I went to(1) Hokkaido and Tohoku. One of the places I went to was Akita City. I went there to visit(2) some friends and to see(3) the Kanto Festival. Since childhood, the performers in the Kanto Festival learn how to(4) balance lantern poles on their hands, hips, shoulders, and head. At first(5), the bamboo poles are not very(6) tall, but little by(7) little they are made taller and taller. It can be dangerous, but if(8) the pole starts falling or a lantern catches fire, the performers know exactly what to do(9). They quickly pick up the pole and start(10) balancing it again. I was so impressed, and had a lot of fun!

2. Cat Cafés

Do you know about "cat cafés"? You can drink(1) coffee at them like in normal cafés, but cats live there and customers can play with them. I first heard about(2) cat cafés recently. I was very surprised. In Canada, we don't(3) have them. I was in Tokyo in August, so I thought it was a good idea to go to one to play(4) with the cats. I went to one in Akihabara. The name is NekoJaLaLa. Eight cute cats live there. It's important to be nice to the cats. You can read(5) a guidebook at the cat café. It tells you what to do(6). For example, you have to(7) follow certain rules. The first rule is that you must(8) wash your hands before touching the cats. Also, you should not (9) surprise the cats. The mood of a cat café is very nice if(10) you follow the rules. Cat cafés are a lot of fun. Please try one sometime!

あいづち Comment Reading　　　Aizuchi Comment Reading

前のセクション「伝言 Message」の本文を使って、ペアの相手の話に相づちをうったり、話を広げたりしましょう。

1. ペアでそれぞれ「伝言 Message」を読む練習をする。
2. じゃんけんをして、話し手と相づちをうつ人を決める。
3. 話し手がメッセージを読み始めるが、1 文読むたびにペアの相手はあいづちを入れていく。
4. 一通り読めたら交代をする。

Using the texts from the previous section, "Dengon Message," listen to your partner's story and make commentary.

1. Practice reading "Dengon Message" as a pair.
2. Play rock-paper-scissors to decide roles.
3. Read the text one sentence at a time. After each sentence, insert one comment.
4. When finished, switch roles.

<使える英語表現集> I see. ／ Oh, really? ／ I didn't know that. ／ That's interesting! ／ I can't believe it. ／ Tell me more. ／ Wow! ／ Is it true? ／ I think that ( ). ／ It's ( ). ／ I don't think so. ／ How ( ) it is! ／ What a ( ) it is! ／ What do you ( )? ／ Why ( )? ／ How many ( )? など

4技能5領域					評価の観点		
読む	聞く	発表	やり取り	書く	知識・技能	思考・判断・表現	主体的に取り組む態度
○	○	(○)	○		○	○	○

< One More Try! >

短い相づちに加えて、質問をしたりコメントを返したりしながら、自然な会話になるように話題を広げていくこともできます。また、友達同士で発表するのもいいでしょう。

あいづち Comment Reading

This summer vacation, I went to Hokkaido and Tohoku.

That's nice!

One of the places I went to was Akita City.

Why did you go there?

I went there to visit some friends and to see the Kanto Festival.

Wow!

活発 Negotiation

Kappatsu Negotiation

Negotiation は「交渉」や「折衝」という意味です。ここでは、英語でやり取りをしながら、ぜひ交渉力を高めていきましょう。

1. ペアになり、ページの場面設定を読み、状況を把握する。
2. じゃんけんをして、交渉する人と交渉される人を決める。
3. 先生の合図で、重要なポイントを伝えながら交渉を始め、3分間で会話は終了とする。交渉される側は、相手の話に英語で対応して、すぐには「OK！」と言わないように、交渉成立ポイントを図る。
4. 終了 20 秒前の合図で、交渉成立に十分な話が聞けたと判断したら、「OK, you can do it.」と答えてあげましょう。

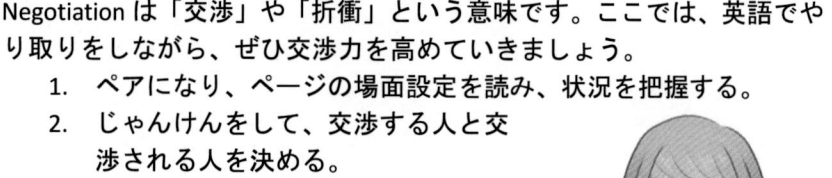

With this activity, students increase their ability to negotiate while communicating in English.

1. Make pairs, read the scenario, and make sure you understand the situation.
2. Play rock-paper-scissors to decide roles.
3. At the teacher's signal, the pair will discuss for 3 minutes. Try not to give in and say "OK!" too easily.
4. When 20 seconds remain, the teacher should give another signal. During this 20 seconds, the negotiator's partner should decide if they made a convincing argument.

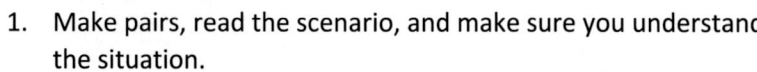

4技能5領域					評価の観点		
読む	聞く	発表	やり取り	書く	知識・技能	思考・判断・表現	主体的に取り組む態度
○	○	○		○	○	○	○

< One more try! >

ここでは、交渉される側も交渉力を発揮しましょう。相手の提案や意見に対して、賛成・反対する理由を英語で述べていき、納得できる内容で話がまとまったら、気持ちよく「OK, you can do it.」と答えてあげてください。

　学校から帰り道、あなたは、河原で子猫が一匹、寒そうに座っている姿を見つけます。そっと抱き上げて頭をなでると、その子猫がにっこり笑ったように見えました。ぜひ、連れて帰って家族の一員として飼いたい。ただ、あなたの家では、これまで動物を飼ったことがありません。

　そこで、あなたはどのように家族を説得しますか。

On your way home from school, you see a cat sitting on the riverbank, looking cold. You gently pick it up and pat it on the head, and it seems to smile at you. You would love to bring him home and keep him as a member of my family. However, you have never had an animal in your home before.

How would you persuade your family to do so?

左の場面で、あなたはどのように相手と交渉していきますか。どんなポイントを強調しますか。話し方のトーンはどのようにしましょうか。

まずは、アピールポイントを考えて、ペアの相手に「OK, you can do it.」と言ってもらえる話を展開していきましょう。交渉相手は、話をよく聞いて、質問したり切り返したりしながら、交渉に応じるかどうかを決めてください。

活発 Negotiation　　　　　　　No. 2　　　　Date:

　学校から帰り道、あなたは、河原で子トラが一匹、寒そうに座って
いる姿を見つけます。そっと抱き上げて頭をなでると、その子トラがに
っこり笑ったように見えました。ぜひ、連れて帰って家族の一員として
飼いたい。ただ、あなたの家では、これまでトラを飼ったことがありま
せん(おそらくどの家族も飼ったことはないでしょうね)。
　そこで、あなたはどのように家族を説得しますか。

On your way home from school, you see a small tiger cub sitting on
the riverbank, looking cold. You gently pick it up and pat it on the head,
and it seems to smile at you. You would love to bring him home and
keep him as a member of my family. However, you have never had a
tiger in your home before. (Probably no family ever has.)
How would you persuade your family to do so?

左の場面で、あなたはどのように相手と交渉していきますか。どんなポイントを強調しますか。話し方のトーンはどのようにしましょうか。
まずは、アピールポイントを考えて、ペアの相手に「OK, you can do it.」と言ってもらえる話を展開していきましょう。交渉相手は、話をよく聞いて、質問したり切り返したりしながら、交渉に応じるかどうかを決めてください。

友達と一緒に学校からの帰り道、あなたは、公園でドラえもんの「どこでもドア」を見つけました。ドアの正面には「30分だけ、しかも1度だけなら使ってもよい」との張り紙がしてあります。

友達は宇宙ステーションに行きたいと言いますが、あなたはアマゾンの大自然でたくさんの動物を見てみたい。そこで、あなたはどのように友達を説得しますか。

On your way home from school with your friends, you find Doraemon's "Dokodemo Door" in the park. On the front of the door, it has a sign that says, "You may use this door only for 30 minutes, and only once." Your friend wants to go to the space station, but you want to see the wilderness of the Amazon and all the animals. How will you persuade your friend to go?

左の場面で、あなたはどのように相手と交渉していきますか。どんなポイントを強調しますか。話し方のトーンはどのようにしましょうか。

まずは、アピールポイントを考えて、ペアの相手に「OK, you can do it.」と言ってもらえる話を展開していきましょう。交渉相手は、話をよく聞いて、質問したり切り返したりしながら、交渉に応じるかどうかを決めてください。

活発 Negotiation No. 4 Date:

友達と一緒に学校からの帰り道、友達と文化祭でのクラスの出し物の話になりました。あなたは、クラス全員で参加できるミュージカルをやってみたいと思いますが、友達は、ホットケーキを焼いてクラスカフェを開くのがいいと言います。友達にも自分の意見に賛成してもらうには、あなたはどのように説得しますか。

On your way home from school with your friends, you and your friends are talking about your class's performance at the cultural festival. You would like to do a musical that the whole class can participate in, but your friend says that you should bake pancakes and have a class café. How would you convince your friend to agree with you?

左の場面で、あなたはどのように相手と交渉していきますか。どんなポイントを強調しますか。話し方のトーンはどのようにしましょうか。
まずは、アピールポイントを考えて、ペアの相手に「OK, you can do it.」と言ってもらえる話を展開していきましょう。交渉相手は、話をよく聞いて、質問したり切り返したりしながら、交渉に応じるかどうかを決めてください。